THE LOVE STORY OF

_____

AND

_____

Other Giftbooks by Exley:
Love Quotations   Love a Celebration
To my very Special Love The Crazy World of Love
My Wedding Planner   Wedding Guest Book
To my very special Wife To my very special Husband
Marriage a Keepsake   Happy Anniversary

BORDER ILLUSTRATIONS BY MARIA TERESA MELONI

Copyright © Helen Exley 1995
ISBN 1-85015-529-1

Edited and pictures selected by Helen Exley.
Designed by Pinpoint Design.
Picture research by P.A.Goldberg and J.M.Clift, Image Select,
London.
Typeset by Delta, Watford.
Printed at Oriental Press, – UAE.

Exley Publications Ltd., 16 Chalk Hill, Watford, Herts. WDl 4BN.
Exley Giftbooks, 232 Madison Avenue, Suite 1206, NY 10016, USA.

OUR LOVE STORY
A Record Book

EDITED BY

HELEN EXLEY

EXLEY

NEW YORK • WATFORD, UK

INTRODUCTION

Meeting, falling in love and then going on to build a life together – these are often the happiest, most exciting things that happen in a lifetime. Everyone has an individual story to tell about their own particular romance – OUR LOVE STORY provides the perfect framework for recording these special memories.

This book makes a lovely gift for a young couple starting out in life together, or a romantic gift from one partner to another – it can be completed at any age by anyone with a love to remember. It gives you the opportunity to tell your own love story, so that you can look back on happy memories, add to it as your life together changes or share it with your close friends or family.

When completed, this book will tell your personal story, and in years to come it will remain as a lasting record of the wonder of falling in love and your precious times together.

CONTENTS

HOW WE FIRST MET   8

FIRST ATTRACTION   10

FALLING IN LOVE   12

OUR FIRST DAYS TOGETHER   14

ROMANTIC MEMORIES   16

GROWING CLOSER   18

MAGIC MOMENTS   21

FAMILY AND FRIENDS   22

OUR COMMITMENT TO EACH OTHER   26

BEAUTIFUL WORDS   27

THE BOOKS WE'VE LOVED   28

SHOWS AND MOVIES WE'VE LOVED   29

SPECIAL PLACES   31

TRAVELS TOGETHER   32

THE LOVES WE SHARE   34

LAUGHING TOGETHER   38

OUR HOME   40

THE OTHER PEOPLE IN OUR LIVES   42

OUR FAMILY 44

THE SADDEST TIMES 48

MISSING YOU 50

LOVE LETTERS 52

HOW OUR LOVE HAS CHANGED 54

LEARNING TO LIVE TOGETHER 56

QUARRELS, FIGHTS AND MAKING UP! 58

PROBLEMS 60

LESSONS WE'VE LEARNED 62

FALLING IN LOVE AGAIN 64

IMPORTANT ANNIVERSARIES 66

OUR HAPPIEST MEMORIES 68

WHEN LOVE IS FOREVER 70

MY PROMISE TO YOU 72

PHOTOGRAPHS, LETTERS AND MEMENTOES 76

Extra blank pages for important additions...

ACKNOWLEDGEMENTS 88

How we first met

FIRST ATTRACTION

WHAT YOU FIRST NOTICED ABOUT EACH OTHER, WHAT YOU LIKED...

FALLING IN LOVE

OUR FIRST DAYS TOGETHER

A PARTICULARLY SPECIAL EARLY MEETING, YOUR FIRST DATES, GETTING TO KNOW EACH OTHER.

PAGE 15

ROMANTIC MEMORIES

GROWING CLOSER

PAGE 18

MAGIC MOMENTS

PAGE 21

SOME HAPPY, SPECIAL MEMORIES YOU SHARE.

Family and friends

PAGE 22

HOW THEY REACTED, WHAT THEY SAID ABOUT YOUR LOVE.

OUR COMMITMENT TO EACH OTHER

YOUR WEDDING DAY OR ANY OTHER SIGNIFICANT DAY WHEN YOU MADE YOUR COMMITMENT.

PAGE 25

BEAUTIFUL WORDS

QUOTES, SAYINGS AND POEMS WHICH MEAN A LOT TO YOU.

THE BOOKS WE'VE LOVED

SHOWS AND MOVIES WE'VE LOVED

SPECIAL PLACES

TRAVELS TOGETHER

THE LOVES WE SHARE

INTERESTS, HOBBIES, PASSIONS, BELIEFS...

THE LOVES WE SHARE

PAGE 37

LAUGHING TOGETHER

FOR FUNNY INCIDENTS, MINOR DISASTERS – ANYTHING FUNNY YOU'VE SHARED.

OUR HOME

THE OTHER PEOPLE IN OUR LIVES

FRIENDS AND OTHER PEOPLE WHO ARE IMPORTANT TO YOU.

PAGE 43

OUR FAMILY

CHILDREN, RELATIVES AND PETS!

OUR FAMILY

THE SADDEST TIMES

Missing you

THE TIMES YOU'VE FELT ALONE AND HOW YOU'VE KEPT LOVE ALIVE.

LOVE LETTERS

FOR YOUR ACTUAL LOVE LETTERS OR COPIED HIGHLIGHTS!

How our love has changed

THE WAY YOUR LOVE HAS GROWN THROUGH THE YEARS.

LEARNING TO LIVE TOGETHER

PROBLEMS

HOW YOU'VE BOTH REACTED TO, AND OVERCOME, DIFFICULTIES YOU'VE HAD TO FACE.

MY PROMISE TO YOU
PAGE 72

YOUR PLEDGE FOR THE FUTURE.

Acknowledgements

Exley Publications is very grateful to the following individuals and organizations for permission to reproduce their pictures. Whilst all reasonable efforts have been made to clear copyright and acknowledge sources and artists, Exley Publications would be happy to hear from any copyright holder who may have been omitted.

COVER: **The Kiss,** Gustav Klimt (1862-1918), Belvedere Gallery, Vienna, Archiv für Kunst.

PAGE 1: **Morning in the Studio,** Patrick William Adam (1854-1930), Fine Art Photographic Library Ltd.

PAGE 4: **Tea in the Garden,** August Wenderhals, Josef Mensing Gallery, Hamm-Rhynern, The Bridgeman Art Library.

PAGE 11: **Picknick,** Paul von Szinyei Merse (1845-1920), Museum der Schönen Kunste, Budapest, Archiv für Kunst.

PAGE 13: **The Poppy Field,** Alphonse Asselbergs (1839-1916), by courtesy of Galerie Berko, Fine Art Photographic Library Ltd.

PAGE 17: **Snow scene – Wanstead Park,** Nils Hans Christiansen, Chenil Galleries, London, Bridgeman Art Library.

PAGE 20: **The Pergola,** Pierre Auguste Renoir, Pushkin Museum, Moscow, Scala.

PAGE 23: **Interior with Tea table,** Marcel Rieder (b.1852), Gavin Graham Gallery, London, Bridgeman Art Library.

PAGE 26: **La veranda bagnata,** Gherasimov Aleksandr (1881-1963), Galleria Statale Tret'jakov, Moscow, Scala.

PAGE 30: **The Bay of Biscay, Brittany,** Henry Moret (1856-1931), Hermitage, St. Petersburg, The Bridgeman Art Library.

PAGE 35: Lucy Willis © 1995, Chris Beetles Gallery, London.

PAGE 39: **An Eygptian Window,** Geraldine Girvan, Chris Beetles Gallery, London.

PAGE 41: **All Aflame,** Brenda Evans, Pheonix Galleries, London, The Bridgeman Art Library.

PAGE 45: **Lilla' al sole,** Claude Monet (1840-1926), Pushkin Museum, Moscow, Scala.

PAGE 49: **Shadows,** Eileen Hogan, The Fine Art Society, London, The Bridgeman Art Library.

PAGE 51: **Die Stickerin,** Georg Friedrich Kersting (1785-1847), Narodowe Museum, Warschau, Archiv für Kunst.

PAGE 55: Roy Hammond, Chris Beetles Gallery, London.

PAGE 57: **The Pride of Dijon,** 1879, William John Hennesy (1839-1917), Cooley Gallery, Old Lyme, Connecticut, Bridgeman Art Library.

PAGE 59: Lucy Willis © 1995, Chris Beetles Gallery, London.

PAGE 61: **White Tulips,** Lucy Willis © 1995, Chris Beetles Gallery, London.

PAGE 64: **The Kiss,** Theophile Alexandre Steinlen (1859-1923), Archiv für Kunst.

PAGE 67: **Tulips for a January Morning,** Timothy Easton, Private Collection, The Bridgeman Art Library.

PAGE 71: **Portrait of Monsieur and Madame Thaulow,** Roll, Petit Palais Paris, Bulloz.

PAGE 73: **Still Life of Flowers,** Eugene Henri Cauchois (1850-1911), Gavin Graham Gallery, London, The Bridgeman Art Library.

PAGE 75: **Love,** 1895, Gustav Klimt, (1862-1918), Museum der Stadt Wien, Archiv für Kunst.

PAGE 83: **Christobel finds Geraldine,** William Gersham Collingwood (1854-1932) by courtesy of Martin Ham, Fine Art Photographic Library Ltd.

PAGE 89: **Where the pale moonbeams linger,** John Atkinson Grimshaw (1836-1893), Christopher Wood Gallery, London, The Bridgeman Art Library.